CW00863857

THE SIEVE

original solo scenes

HEATHER STEPHENS

with a new adaptation of
Hans Christian Andersen's
THE LITTLE MATCH GIRL

DRAMATIC LINES, TWICKENHAM, ENGLAND
text copyright © Heather Stephens

Dramatic Lines PO Box 201
Twickenham TW2 5RQ
England

ISBN 0 9522224 0 X

The Sieve first published 1993 by Dramatic Lines, Twickenham, England. All rights reserved

Printed by The K&N Press Ltd., West Molesey, Surrey, England

Monologues impose a discipline on the performer with a need for the material to be clear and incisive. The nature of a solo dramatic piece means that there is no 'sounding board' or interaction from other actors only the response from the audience.

For a solo performance the actor needs to develop speech much as either soloist singer or musician does within the framework of music. Thus it is vital to obtain the right monologue material.

In my acting experience good monologues are hard to find. Appropriate material is invaluable for auditions and for the use of children and students in a variety of situations.

The pieces in this book have been written to provide something new and exciting. I hope they will encourage young people for whom they are especially written.

I wish every success to those who use them.

Peter Egan

Acknowledgments
My very grateful thanks to:
Shaun McKenna, Principal of Examinations, LAMDA
Penny Phillips, EnsorSpeak
for their invaluable advice and encouragement
and to:
Jenny Thornton for the work involved
in the trial of scenes

CONTENTS

A GAME OF CHICKEN

'LACES' BECAME STREETWISE AT A FRIGHTENINGLY YOUNG AGE, IS OUTWARDLY FULL OF BRAVADO AND TOTALLY DISTRUSTFUL OF AUTHORITY AND ADULT INTENTION - AN INNER CITY PRODUCT WITH SPEECH AND DEFENSIVE BODY LANGUAGE TO BE FOUND IN ANY URBAN REGION.

A CHAIR CENTRE STAGE, *ISOLATED. 'LACES' PINNED DOWN ON THE CHAIR - TRAPPED BY OFFICIALDOM, STARING OUT DEFIANTLY UPWARDS AT IMAGINED ADULT SEATED BEHIND A DESK BEYOND IN THE AUDITORIUM.*

LACES: (Shrugging)
We've played for a while.
What's that got to do with you?

PAUSE

(Impatiently)
'Course we always use the same place.
It's no use if the cars ain't got up no speed.
Is it?
Duel carriageway's the only place for it.
You've no idea; you don't know nothink!

PAUSE

'E was ace.

LACES STANDS

'E was ace from day one: 'E started the game.

LACES MOVES FORWARD SLOWLY.
HALTS

We was all standing about.
Nothink to do, as usual.
(Smiling at the memory)
We was by the road.
All of a sudden 'E yelled 'CHICKEN'
and 'E was gone!
Carried on shoutin 'n wavin 'till
'E'd made it.

LACES WAVES WILDLY

Then 'E shouted 'LACES'
An' I went.
An' 'E carried on shouting 'till we was all across.

1

LACES MOVES FORWARD

LACES: It felt good; everyone cheerin, laughing.
An' headlights trying ter stab at you
through the dark.
Running; like you never run before,
heart beating loud.
Like the best ever fair-ride,
free whenever you want,
it turned out to be.

LACES ALIVE WITH JOY

Always the same, reaching the other side.
However many times you done it.
Magic!

PAUSE, LONG SIGH

Oh! Yeah! 'E was always last across.
'Ed judge the run, time it.
Concentrate hard: 'E always knew when.
Told you, 'E was the best.
(Outburst)
Course somethin went wrong!
'E wouldn't be dead otherwise!

LACES MOVEMENTS BECOME AGGITATED,
LACES TURNS TO AVOID ADULT SCRUTINY

(Quieter, calmer)
This last time, I'd reached the other side...

LACES LOOKS BACK, RELIVES

...Looking back, 'E'd only just started the run.
Cutting it fine, I thought.
Then...
...Then, a sports car shot from nowhere.
Overtook everything in sight, wrong side've the road.

LACES COVERS EYES

Brakes screeching: someone screamed after that.
A loud thud. So fast I couldn't take it in,
none of it.

LACES LOWERS HANDS SLOWLY
PAUSES, SHAKING HEAD

(Without emotion)
'E didn't stand a chance.

LACES SEARCHES ALONG FRONT OF STAGE
BENDS DOWN

LACES: (Whispering tenderly)
When I got to 'Im; 'E looked straight up at me.
But 'E talked too quiet, couldn't catch what 'E
wanted to say...

LACES LOOKS DIRECTLY AT THE FIGURE OF AUTHORITY
SEATED BEHIND THE DESK

...Only heard 'Im say 'Mum'.

LACES MOVES AS IF TO ENVELOP THE FIGURE LYING
BY THE ROADSIDE.
LACES LIES ABSOLUTELY STILL.

THE BRIDESMAID

HANNAH WAS THRILLED TO DISCOVER THAT HER DEAREST WISH HAD COME TRUE – SHE HAD BEEN CHOSEN TO BE A BRIDESMAID. HOWEVER, HER INITIAL DELIGHT HAS BEEN SHORT LIVED AND ANY HAPPINESS HAS EVAPORATED. HANNAH NOW FINDS HERSELF IN THE DEPTHS OF DESPAIR SUFFERING A HEADCOLD... BUT THE COMMON COLD HAS LITTLE TO DO WITH HER UTTER DESPERATION.

HANNAH PACES, EYES GLUED TO THE FLOOR. SHE IS WEARING A VERY FLATTERING NEUTRAL COLOUR.

HANNAH: I could **scream!**
(Long pause)
Cripes!
Poor **me!**

SHE SLOWS DOWN AND SNIFFS LOUDLY

Can you believe it?

SHE STANDS STILL AND PAUSES FOR THOUGHT

Waited **years;** every friend I've ever had's
been a bridesmaid at least once.
Then!
At long last, when it's **my** turn...

SHE SHAKES HER FISTS IN ANGRY FRUSTRATION

...DISASTER!
(Loud sniff)
Should've known it was too good to be true.
I was so **happy**
and **grateful** when I found out...
(Pause)
...Told everybody!
So absolutely **everybody** knows.
(Quietly)
Poor, poor me.
(Sniff)
Cripes! They'll **all** want to see the photos after.
Bound to, aren't they?
Even the ones who're not there on the day!

SHE BLOWS HER NOSE VIOLENTLY

Then there's the **hundreds** of people
who'll be 'At the Wedding'...
...they'll all be looking!

*SHE ADOPTS A SEDATE POSE AND DRIFTS THEATRICALLY WITH
AN IMAGINARY BASKET HANDLE HELD BETWEEN FINGERS
SHE STOPS AND STANDS AND SMILES IN A SUPERIOR SARCASTIC
FASHION
SHE SNIFFS GENTEELLY*

HANNAH: Cousin Becky was a bridesmaid when she was three.
Looked as pretty as a peach!
And behaved **ABOMINABLY!**
Threw a screaming wobbly in church.
(Sniff)
Did anyone mind?
(Pause)
No!
(Bitterly)
'Cause Becky looked like a china doll.
(Vindictively)
A little Victorian doll...
(Enviously)
...With a tiny flower basket
and a beautiful beautiful rustling lace-trimmed dress
with bows and stiff petticoats.

SHE SNIFFS LOUDLY

ME!
Cripes! I'll roll down the aisle looking more
like a lemon past its sell by date.

SHE HANGS HER HEAD

(Muttering under her breath)
Never live it down, never ever.
(Pause)
My dress is **FOUL!**
(Forcefully)
FOUL! Believe me...
...Boat neck, puff sleeves, ferociously
yellow
and **cheap**-looking.
(Sniff)
I shan't forget that jaunt to the Bridal Boutique in a hurry,
I can tell you.
Nightmare!
Nightmare, no other word for it.
'Unusual choice of colour,' said the sales assistant safe in grey.
'The bride is looking for something a little
different, I can tell.'

5

HANNAH: A foul yellow horror was whipped off the rail
ballooning in mid-air as she thrust it at me!
My heart sank.

SHE CROSSES HER FINGERS AND CLOSES HER EYES

Don't let it fit, please.
Don't let it fit.
(Sniff)
Hmmm.
(Brightly)
Three sizes too large.
(Pause)
But did that do me any good?
No!

SHE MOVES A STEP OR TWO AND STARES AHEAD

I stood there on pale pink carpet;
my face burning red.
I turned to look into the long mirrors.
(Sniff)
But I couldn't see myself; I wasn't anywhere
to be seen.
Instead, something like a citrus fruit bobbed
into view and all the mirrors were filled with yellow.
Looked like lemons piled high on a market stall
squeezed together.
(Pause)
Did the ground swallow me up?
No.
'She'll grow into it easily by the wedding,'
promised the sales assistant.

SHE SNEEZES AND REACHES FOR A HANDKERCHIEF

No chance!
Tried it on again, just now.
I haven't grown a centimetre.
(Sniff)
Cripes! The wedding's Saturday.
Doesn't leave much time for growing, does it?
(Muttering to herself)
Poor, poor me... poor...... me.

SHE WANDERS OFF DESPONDENTLY
BLOWS HER NOSE LOUDLY

THE PENGUIN

CHRIS IS AN ENDEARING TOMBOY WHO ATTRACTS TROUBLE AND RARELY LEARNS FROM PAST MISTAKES AND HAS YET TO UNDERSTAND THAT TAKING IS STEALING. THE CHIRPY CHEERFUL CHILD IS RETURNING FROM THE SECOND SCHOOL VISIT TO A ZOO. CHRIS IS DRESSED CASUALLY AND CARRIES A DUFFLE BAG.

CHRIS RACES FROM THE COACH AND GRINDS TO A HALT IN RESPONSE TO AN UNHEARD COMMAND AND TURNS TO FACE THE TEACHER ADOPTING A SLOUCH THAT IS NEITHER TO ATTENTION NOR AT EASE. CHRIS CAREFULLY AND PROVOCATIVELY PLACES THE BAG ON THE GROUND AND STARES HARD AT IT.

CHRIS: Sorry... Sir!

PAUSE FOR AN UNHEARD REMARK
CHRIS SHUFFLES

No!
I didn't hear you tell us not to run
when we got off the coach.

PAUSE FOR AN UNHEARD RETORT

Yes! Everybody else must've.
Suppose I can'tve been listening.
(Sneaking a look at the bag)
It was a pretty fair day out, I'd say.

CHRIS LISTENS TO AN UNHEARD QUESTION

No! I didn't do anything I shouldn't!
(Pause)
Not like last time the class went to the zoo.

PAUSE FOR AN UNHEARD REMARK

(Sulkily)
I know it caused trouble for the school and for Mum;
it caused trouble all round.
But you've been watching me all day; I couldn'tve
done anything today.
Any case, I said I wouldn't ever do anything
like that again.

CHRIS LISTENS AND HASTILY JUMPS IN WITH A RESPONSE WHILST SHAKING HEAD

No!
No! I haven't forgotten what you said about being lucky to be
allowed to go because of what happened the last time.

CHRIS TAKES IN AN UNHEARD QUESTION

CHRIS: There's nothing in the bag, honest!
Only leftovers.
Look for youself
if you don't believe me, then Sir!

*CHRIS WRENCHES OPEN THE BAG AND PULLS OUT A FLATTENED
DRINKS CARTON, A CRUST AND EMPTY CRISP BAG AND THROWS
THEM ASIDE BEFORE HOLDING THE BAG UPSIDE DOWN AND
SHAKING IT HARD*

(Muttering)
Said I wouldn't do it again!

*REACTING TO AN UNHEARD COMMENT CHRIS LOOKS UP
BEFORE PICKING UP THE OFFENDING LITTER
AND THRUSTING IT BACK IN THE BAG*

No, I don't make a habit of throwing litter about.

CHRIS LISTENS TO A BRIEF QUESTION

Why? Don't know really.
I didn't think of it as stealing;
didn't know it was going to happen.
It just came to me at the time...
(Pause)
...wanting a penguin.

CHRIS LISTENS TO A FURTHER QUESTION

Easy!
I nipped over the wall, caught the slow one
and popped it into the bag.
It went quiet straight away, must've gone to sleep
in the dark.
(Pause)
Bag was heavy to carry for the rest of the day,
I can tell you!
It was only a small one!
Penguins are heavier than they look!

CHRIS LISTENS TO A FURTHER QUESTION WITH INTEREST

Oh! Mum said she was suspicious from the first.
Since when had I ever rushed in and gone straight up
and run a bath?
She'd never known me want a bath.
She went berserk when she barged in and saw it!
Said I was stupid.

CHRIS: It's not stupid to want something...
...even if you do have to give it back.

CHRIS SHRUGS AWAY A BRIEF COMMENT

Don't you know what happened after that?
Well! Mum phoned Mister Taylor at the school.
And **he** phoned the zoo.
And I made friends with my penguin in the bathroom.
Seemed like no time
before the van from the zoo arrived
to take it back.

CHRIS LISTENS TO A FRIENDLY WARNING

I said I wouldn't do it again!
And I haven't.
(Quietly)
But I'm not sorry I did it in the first place.
It was good while it lasted.
(Pause)
I had something nobody else had.
I had a penguin and I called it Chris:
same name as me.
(Pause)
Matter of fact I was keeping an eye out for Chris
today; couldn't seem to see any slow penguins.
Not today, don't know why?

CHRIS PICKS UP THE DUFFLE BAG AND WANDERS OFF

EXIT CHRIS.

THE FAIRY QUEEN

LOUISE HAS JUST DISCOVERED THAT A CLASSMATE HAS BEEN GIVEN THE LEAD ROLE IN THE FORTHCOMING STAGE PRODUCTION. LOUISE HAD SET HER HEART ON PLAYING THE FAIRY QUEEN AND IS NOW FORCED TO FACE UP TO THE BIGGEST DISAPPOINTMENT OF HER LIFE.

ENTER: LOUISE, DOWNCAST WITH EYES GLUED TO THE FLOOR. SHE CROSSES THE STAGE, REJECTION AND HUMILIATION EXPRESSED IN SLOUCHED BODY AND DRAGGED LIFELESS STEPS. SHE HALTS.

LOUISE: (Bitterly to herself)
But **I** wanted to be the Fairy Queen.

SHE TURNS TO ADDRESS THE AUDIENCE DIRECTLY

(Sweetly)
With a magic wand
and a beautiful white floating dress.
(Pause)
And wings!

SHE SIGHS, TOUCHING HER HAIR

And diamonds and stars in my hair.

SHE TURNS AWAY, TAKING A FEW DAINTY STEPS. SWINGING BACK AGGRESSIVELY, HANDS ON HIPS

(Sulkily)
Don't want to be in the show at all, now!
I don't want to be anything
if I can't be the Fairy Queen.

SHE PAUSES, TWISTING FINGERS IN ANGUISH

(Directly to the audience)
She's not even going to have
a proper fairy wand, anyway.
I know for sure; I've seen for myself!
It's just a stick
with a tinsel star at the top.
Worn-out looking: all the magic gone.

SHE MOVES CLOSER TO REVEAL HER SECRET

I saw it by accident.
There was a cardboard box tucked out of sight.
(Gesturing behind)
In the corner of the back room.
And the wand was sticking up, out of the box.
With the wings.
Hmm; and those looked more like bent coat hangers
than real fairy wings, too!

SHE SIGHS LOUDLY, SHRUGS HER SHOULDERS

LOUISE: I wonder.
If I close my eyes and turn around three times,
just like they do in Fairy tales.
Perhaps...

SHE CLOSES EYES TIGHTLY, CONCENTRATES HARD

(Whispering, turning slowly)
I wish.
I wish.
I wish.

*SHE STRETCHES OUT A HAND ATTEMPTING TO CATCH HOLD
OF A NON-EXISTENT WAND.
SHE FEELS FOR WINGS, A HEADDRESS
BEFORE OPENING HER EYES*

(Bitterly disappointed)
Nothing's happened!

PAUSE

I knew it wouldn't.

*SHE ROCKS ON HER FEET.
HER FACE AND BODY BECOME ANIMATED.
A CUNNING ARTFUL LOOK CROSSES HER FACE*

I've an idea for a much, much better wish.
That will **really** work.

*SHE COVERS HER EYES WITH HER FINGERS, HUMMING TO
HERSELF AND COMMENCES TO TURN SLOWLY*

(Confidently)
I wish.
I wish more than anything...

*SHE STANDS ABSOLUTELY STILL AND LOWERS HER HANDS
REVEALING TIGHTLY SCREWED-UP EYE LIDS*

...That Tricia will fall sick with mumps
and measles.

(Gleefully)
And be covered from head to toe
in massive angry spots!
(Pause)
So **I** can be Fairy Queen.

*SHE OPENS ONE EYE AT A TIME
SMILES TRIUMPHANTLY
AND SKIPS OFF HAPPILY*

EXIT LOUISE.

11

THE SIEVE

JO IS TOTALLY WITHDRAWN AND HAS CHOSEN TO REMAIN SILENT – AN ELECTIVE MUTE. JO ATTENDS A 'SPECIAL' SCHOOL FOR BOYS AND GIRLS WHO FIND LEARNING DIFFICULT. PUPILS LIKE JO EXPERIENCE INSURMOUNTABLE DIFFICULTY IN MAKING FRIENDS AND FITTING IN WITH ADULTS... BUT JO HAS FOUND THE ANSWER.

ENTER: JO, WALKING NEITHER QUICKLY NOR SLOWLY, A KITCHEN SIEVE HELD TIGHT TO THE FACE.
JO HALTS, VIEWING THE AUDIENCE WITH AN EXAGGERATED SWEEPING MOVEMENT. JO PEEKS FROM BEHIND THE SIEVE, FACE HALF-IN, HALF-OUT. JO RELUCTANTLY WITHDRAWS THE SIEVE FROM THE FACE WHILST LOOKING UP AT AN IMAGINARY MOTHER.

JO: I walk to school,
               every morning with Mum:
               after cornflakes or toast.
               And no one talks to me.
               Ever.

JO LOOKS DOWN AT THE SIEVE; AND UP, KNOWINGLY

But grown-ups talk to Mum.
People like old Mrs Parker touch her sleeve
and take her aside.
And whisper not quite quietly enough.

JO SMILES

I know what they're whispering about:
I know why they don't want me to hear.
It's obvious.
They're talking about, **ME!**

JO RETREATS BEHIND THE SIEVE AND STANDS STIFFLY
JO DRAWS THE SIEVE ASIDE

A grown-up is examining me with, **'A Look'.**
'What's she/(he) wearing **that** for?'
Mum looks embarrassed every time.
(Quickly)
'Why! Jo's playing.'
Mum gets that in quickly.
(Pause)
Then, that grown-up stares so hard
that I shrivel-up inside.
(Pause)
'Playing at what?'
Asks the nosey grown-up.

JO SHRINKS SMALL

JO: Mum has worked out a reply.
'Jo's fond of acting;
she's/(he's) pretending!
You know!'
But Old Mrs Nosey Parker
or Old Mrs Whatever-It-Is
doesn't know.
'Pretending to be what?' hisses the grown-up.

*JO PULLS THE SIEVE OVER THE FACE, STANDS AS STILL AS A
STATUE BEFORE SLIDING OUT FROM BEHIND THE SIEVE.*

I wait for Mum to say...

JO LOWERS THE SIEVE IN RESIGNED MANNER

(Whispering)
Concord.

*JO RUNS A SHORT DISTANCE WITH SIEVE HELD TO THE FACE.
PAUSES, WHIPPING AWAY SIEVE STARING OUT AT THE AUDIENCE*

CONCORD!
No wonder I'm stared at!

*JO PAUSES IN HURT BEWILDERMENT
AND RETREATS BEHIND THE SIEVE TAKING TWO OR THREE
WEIGHTLESS STEPS*

(Peeping out from behind the sieve)
Other times Mum'll say...
'A spaceman walking on the moon.'
And they both look down on me with tight little
smiles and then talk about the weather.

JO ALLOWS THE SIEVE TO LOWER, DEFEATED

(Sighing)
She has even been known to say...
'A knight in shining armour.'

A LONG PAUSE, JO CAREFULLY EXAMINES THE SIEVE

(Shaking head vehemently)
NO!
I'm none of these. I'm **NOT!**
I'm not pretending; I'm not playing.
I'm **ME,** on my way to school.
Out of reach, I can't be touched.

JO: (Clutching sieve)
I'm safe behind my sieve.
But why?
Why doesn't anyone else understand...

*JO BACKS AWAY, DISTANCING HERSELF/(HIMSELF) WHILST
SHRINKING-UP AND RAISING THE SIEVE*

...That the world's too frightening to face?
Not even Mum seems to understand that.

JO STANDS ABSOLUTELY STILL, THE SIEVE CLASPED TIGHTLY.

SEEN THROUGH A GLASS DARKLY

STACY HAS A GRANDMOTHER SUFFERING FROM SENILE DEMENTIA AND HAS BEEN EXPOSED TO THE IRRATIONAL BEHAVIOUR AND DISTRESSING CONFUSION AND IRRITATING DEMANDS OF AN OLD PERSON WHOSE REAL PERSONALITY HAS LONG SINCE DIED.

STACY SITS, LEGS DANGLING DOWN FROM THE STAGE, SWIGGING FROM A BOTTLE OF COKE. BANGING HEELS AGAINST THE HARD SURFACE SUFFICIENTLY TO PRODUCE A LAZY RHYTHM. STACY RAISES THE BOTTLE TO THE LIGHT AND CAREFULLY OBSERVES THE DARK GASEOUS WORLD WITHIN.

STACY: Gran went doolally!
(Tapping head)
Round the twist!
(Pause)
Mum says...

STACY SWIGS FROM THE BOTTLE

...That's why Gran had ter go somewhere:
'cause she got **confused.**
(Pause)
Funny thing is I didn't think I'd miss 'er.

STACY SWINGS FEET UP AND HUGS KNEES

Came ter stay after Gramps went.
Yonks ago: I was only little.
Thought the world've me, Mum says.
Can't say as I remember.
Gran don't remember nothin' neither.
That's bin 'er trouble!

STACY RELAXES AND SHIFTS POSITION

All I know is Mum couldn't do nothin' right.
Food was never what she fancied!
Stone cold or scalding 'er tongue.
Or the meat was tough as shoe leather.
And Mum'd find out she'd taken out 'er false set
'n hidden 'em somewhere!
She was always leavin' the teeth about the place!
An' then she'd shout for Gramps
over n' over an' get out've order
when'e weren't there ter look fer the teeth.
E'd bin dead and buried years!
Gran was well n'truly off'er trolley!

STACY PLACES THE BOTTLE DOWN CAREFULLY AND STANDS

STACY: It got Mum down.
That... and the knittin'
(Pause)
Gran'd bin tryin' ter knit a string dishcloth!
What a joke!
Gran tryin' ter knit string on great blue plastic
needles like tree trunks!
(Pause)
Mum'd start'er off wiv loads've stitches;
'n Gran'd work down till there was one!
(Pause)
Next she'd shout out n'somebody'd 'ave to push-up
loops n'things.
Didn't matter much, how.
There was massive holes n'loops all over.
(Pause)
Or she'd drop all the stitches in one go!
An' pull n'pull an' end up wiv everythin' undone.

STACY RETRIEVES THE BOTTLE

In the end the string'd bin knitted up so much that it kept on
breaking but she weren't no nearer to a dishcloth!

STACY DRINKS FROM THE BOTTLE

Real trouble was Gran didn't know night from day.
Just like a baby, Mum says.
She'd be knittin' without'er teeth in, shoutin'
'What's the time? I'm famished.'
After a plateful it'd be,
'What's the time? I'm famished.'
Then it'd be,
'What day is it?' n' 'What's the time?'
Day in, day out.
(Pause)
I **hated**'er for making Mum cry.
I'd watch'er fumblin' around for the dirty ball've
string that'd rolled under'er chair;
an' I'd... not hear'er shout n'scream, on purpose.
After, I'd pick up'er string n' push it into'er hand.
I **hated'er** but I knew I shouldn't an' I felt bad.
(Pause)
Got worse, didn't it.

STACY SCREWS THE BOTTLE AROUND IN NERVOUS HANDS

STACY: From then on...
(Painfully)
...she started to hit-out at Mum all the time.
An' taking off all'er clothes n'wakin' us up
in the middle of the night.
(Whispering)
An' screamin' at Mum n'bangin' all the doors.
(Pause)
Tryin' to escape!
Thought she'd bin put in prison.
(Quickly)
She wanted to go to the shops n'Mum were a wicked
wicked bitch ter stop 'er.

STACY DRINKS FROM THE BOTTLE AND WIPES THE BACK OF
A HAND HARD ACROSS THE MOUTH AND GROWS CALMER

(Slowly)
In the end Mum couldn't take it no more.
(Pause)
An'... they took'er away.

STACY EXAMINES FINGERNAILS

Mum goes every week; I ain't never bin.
(Pause)
They're all the same...
(Tapping head meaningfully)
...in there. **Mum** says, no place fer'a child ter visit.
(Pause)
Funny, I miss Gran: **but,** Mum says Gran don't miss me.
She's-as-happy there as anywhere but 'eaven.

STACY SITS, LEGS DANGLING DOWN FROM THE STAGE AS
BEFORE AND BEGINS TO TAP HEELS LAZILY AGAINST THE HARD
SURFACE. STACY RAISES THE HALF-EMPTY BOTTLE UP TO THE
LIGHT AND CAREFULLY OBSERVES THE DARK INPENETRABLE
HALF-WORLD WITHIN.

TELEVISION SPINECHILLER

NIKKI IS HIGHLY SENSITIVE, WITH A MOBILE FACE AND EXPRESSIVE HANDS. NIKKI IS DRESSED IN AN OVERSIZED LONG SLEEVED LOOSE TOP WORN OVER A T SHIRT AND IS WEARING SLIPPERS ON BARE FEET.

A CHAIR FRONT STAGE, FACING AN IMAGINARY TELEVISION SET.
ENTER: NIKKI, WANDERING TOWARDS THE CHAIR WHILST READING ALOUD SNATCHES FROM A NEWSPAPER 'T.V. FILM GUIDE'.

NIKKI: Grim and gripping...
(Pause)
...Master of suspense...

NIKKI STOPS, ENTHRALLED BY THE WRITE-UP
NIKKI MOUTHS WORDS SILENTLY, FEAR... TERROR... HORROR
BEFORE MOVING ON

...Hitchcock.
A must!

NIKKI LOWERS THE NEWSPAPER, GRINNING IMPISHLY

...Definitely **not** for the squeamish!

NIKKI RUSHES FORWARD TO THE IMAGINARY TELEVISION SET
SWITCHES ON, SEEKS CHANNEL STANDING ON THE VERY EDGE
OF THE STAGE BEFORE MOVING THE CHAIR CLOSER
NIKKI SETTLES ON THE CHAIR

She's **alone** in the old house.

NIKKI CONCENTRATES ON THE SCREEN

The murderer's breaking in through a window...

NIKKI'S EYES GROW WIDE

(Gasping)
...Cutting the telephone wires.
(Pause)
Stay downstairs!

THE NEWSPAPER SLIPS TO THE FLOOR UNNOTICED
NIKKI SQUIRMS UNCOMFORTABLY

(Nervously)
OH! Oh **no!**
Please go back down.

NIKKI BECOMES MORE AND MORE AGITATED AND WAVES
HANDS

NIKKI: Run out of the house, there's time to escape.
(Pause)
Don't go up!

NIKKI DRAWS FEET UP ONTO THE CHAIR SEAT
THE SLIPPERS CLATTER TO THE FLOOR
NIKKI TIGHTLY EMBRACES KNEES

(Groaning)
Don't.
(Raised voice)
Don't go into the bathroom, he's behind the door.

NIKKI SHRINKS UP SMALL, EYES GLUED TO THE SCREEN
THEN PULLS THE NECK OF THE LOOSE TOP OVER THE HEAD AND
DISAPPEARS INSIDE THE OVERLARGE GARMENT
NIKKI EMERGES WITH TIGHTLY CLOSED EYES
CAUTIOUSLY THE EYES FLICKER OPEN.

(With surprise)
Oh!
Where's the murderer, then?
He's gone from the bathroom.
She's cleaning her teeth.

NIKKI CAUTIOUSLY RETURNS ONE FOOT AT A TIME
TO THE FLOOR AND LEANS CLOSER TO THE SCREEN

(A sharp intake of breath)
She's going into the bedroom.
The murderer's in there, I know it!
(Whispering)
Perhaps he's hiding under her bed
and she doesn't realise.
Oh no!

NIKKI SWALLOWS HARD, RISING TO A HALF-SITTING
HALF-STANDING POSITION

Oh!

NIKKI FALLS BACK INTO THE CHAIR

She's undressing for bed, now.
(Pause)
DON'T!

GESTURING FRANTICALLY

Please,
please don't sit on the edge of the bed.

NIKKI SITS TRANSFIXED BY THE ACTION
NIKKI SUDDENLY CLASPS HANDS OVER EARS
BEFORE PULLING THE LONG SLEEVES OF THE LOOSE TOP OVER
BOTH HANDS

NIKKI: (Quietly)
There's a hand... coming out from under the bed...
...About to...

A HAND EMERGES FROM NIKKI'S LONG SLEEVE
NIKKI'S HAND POUNCES MIMICKING THE SCREEN ACTION

...Clasp your ankle.
(Turning head)
I can't look!

NIKKI RUNS AND HIDES BEHIND THE CHAIR
NIKKI APPEARS ABOVE THE CHAIRBACK WIDE-EYED

(With surprise)
What happened?
She's alright.
How's that?
What did I miss?

NIKKI CREEPS BACK ONTO THE CHAIR FEELING CHEATED

(With new-found confidence)
She's reading a book in bed; scarey bit's over.
(Yawning aloud)
It'll be the end soon.
Phew! It wasn't **that** bad.

NIKKI SCREAMS LOUDLY, LEAPING UP AND KNOCKING
OVER THE CHAIR AND TURNS TO RUN BLINDLY

EXIT NIKKI.

MUSICAL STATUES

CHARLOTTE IS A PARTY LOVING DRAMA QUEEN, SHE LOVES TO OVERDRESS AND INSISTS UPON WEARING BOWS IN HER HAIR AND SPECIAL PARTY SHOES. CHARLOTTE HAS A HIGHLY COMPETITIVE NATURE AND A DISTINCTIVE VOICE THAT CANNOT BE IGNORED - SHE ALWAYS, ALWAYS GETS HER OWN WAY.

CHARLOTTE STANDS, *SQUARELY FACING THE UNSEEN MOTHER ORGANISING A BIRTHDAY PARTY (MRS PERRY IS OFF STAGE IN THE WINGS, CHARLOTTE WILL ADDRESS HER DIRECTLY AND WILL DELIVER ALL ASIDES TO THE AUDIENCE).*
THE BIRTHDAY PARTY IS IN FULL SWING, A PARTY GAME HAS JUST ENDED AND CHARLOTTE AWAITS INSTRUCTIONS FOR THE NEXT WITH EAGER ANTICIPATION, HER FACE TILTED, EYES GLUED ATTENTIVELY ON MRS PERRY FOR CHARLOTTE IS DESPERATE TO BEGIN.

CHARLOTTE: (Hand shooting up)
But, but Mrs Perry
there's no need to run through the rules.
Everybody knows how to play!
Dance 'till the music stops...

SHE ADOPTS AN EXAGGERATED POSE

...Then freeze.
(A hard edge to the voice)
And you're **out** if you so much as blink!
Or wobble or fall over.

SHE GLOWERS AT PARTYGOERS IN TURN

(ASIDE)   (Smiling knowingly)
And **I'm** going to win!

SHE POSITIONS HERSELF THEATRICALLY
POINTS A TOE AND TOSSES HER HEAD BACK DRAMATICALLY

(ASIDE)   (Gliding off gracefully)
At last!

SHE TWIRLS CAUTIOUSLY IN A TIGHT CIRCLE
MOVING EVER SLOWER – ANTICIPATING.
SHE RETURNS TO HER ORIGINAL POSITION FACING MRS PERRY
AND FREEZES AT LIGHTNING SPEED

(ASIDE)   (Turning neck sharply, casting eyes about)
Oh! Good.
Zoe's out.
And Sarah, fancy that!

SHE MOVES OFF, TWIRLING WITH GREATER CONFIDENCE
USING THE STAGE
SHE FREEZES

(Turning neck sharply, allowing mouth to drop open
looking deeply concerned and utterly serious)

(ASIDE)   Victoria's wobbling all over the place.
                 She's **got** to be out.
                 Even if it is her party.
                 (She pouts)

SHE MOVES OFF ENERGETICALLY
FOLLOWS A MOVEMENT OFF STAGE IN THE WINGS

(Addressing a group clustered around Mrs Perry)
Hard luck, Victoria...

SHE SPINS AROUND QUICKLY

(For the benefit of everyone present)
Don't cry!
It's only a game, Victoria.

SHE IS CAUGHT OFF GUARD AND FORCED TO FREEZE
ON ONE LEG

(ASIDE)   (Turning neck sharply, desperation in her face)
                 I'm going to wobble.
                 I've had it!

SHE MOVES OFF HASTILY

(Triumphantly for the benefit of everyone present)
Got away with it.
Phew!

(ASIDE)   (Leaning forward, quietly but vindictively)
                 ...But Lizianne didn't!

SHE TWIRLS HAPPILY

(Addressing group clustered around Mrs Perry loudly)
Shame, Lizianne!

SHE MOVES OVERCONFIDENTLY, PLAYING TO THE 'AUDIENCE'
IN THE WINGS
SHE FREEZES, OPENLY LOOKING AROUND AND ABOUT
RAISING FOUR FINGERS HIGH: LOWERING A FINGER SMUGLY
THEN ANOTHER BEFORE PRANCING FORWARD

(ASIDE)	Just between the two of us.
	(With a toss of the head)
	Her, and me!

SHE ABANDONS ALL CAUTION.
WOBBLES ON ATTEMPTING THE FREEZE.
DESPITE DESPERATE EFFORTS TO RETAIN POSE
SHE TOPPLES, UNBALANCED

(Screeching at Mrs Perry)
She pushed me, Mrs Perry!
She cheated!

(ASIDE)	(Flouncing forward)
	It's not fair!
	Not fair!

THROWING A TANTRUM

(Addressing Mrs Perry)
Mrs Perry, **I wasn't ready.**
Do it again!

| (ASIDE) | Actually, **she** pushed me! |

SHE STAMPS HER FOOT IN TEMPER

(Rushing towards Mrs Perry)
Again, pleeese!

(ASIDE)	(Muttering to herself, pacing)
	Stupid Victoria.
	Stupid party.
	Stupid, stupid game.

SHE HALTS

(Turning her head calls brightly across to Mrs Perry)
Mrs Perry, Mrs Perry!
Can we play 'Musical Bumps' next?

(ASIDE)	Good!
	(Pause)
	'Cause **I'm** going to win!

SHE RUSHES OFF TO JOIN THE GROUP IN THE WINGS

EXIT CHARLOTTE.

BALLOON RACE

A.J. IS A PLACID OBSERVER WHO CARES LITTLE FOR THE COMPANY OF OTHERS BUT IS CONTENT TO QUIETLY ENJOY EXPERIENCES TO THE FULL IN A DETACHED MANNER WITHOUT NEED OF FRIENDSHIP (A.J. LIVES IN ANOTHER WORLD.) A.J. IS DRESSED IN SCHOOL UNIFORM.

ENTER: A.J. UNHURRIDLY, CAPTIVATED BY A RED HELIUM BALLOON THAT BOBS AND STRAINS ON A TIGHTLY HELD LENGTH OF STRING. AN IMPORTANT-LOOKING LABEL IS CLEARLY VISIBLE DANGLING FROM THE BALLOON. A.J. MOVES FORWARD, EYES FIXED ON THE JEALOUSLY GUARDED OBJECT. TO HALT, INNER CONTENTMENT DISPLAYED IN A HALF-SMILE. A.J. TOYS WITH THE STRING, GENTLY TEASING THE BALLOON.

A.J: Yesterday, we had a balloon race.

A.J. TWEAKS THE STRING

Everyone was there.
All my class, and my teacher.
And the whole of the rest of the school.
Everyone!

A.J. PAUSES, REMEMBERING EVENTS

All those people crowded-up together:
and each one had a balloon.
And I liked just-standing there on the big field:
a little way away, by myself,
with the wind tugging at my red balloon.
(Revealing a serious confidence)
I had to hold-on to that string of mine
ever-so-tight
because my very own balloon was trying and trying
so hard to escape.

A.J. LOOKS ANXIOUSLY AT THE RED BALLOON

Then! Everyone was talking loud.
And the man had to shout...
One, Two, Threee, GO!
And **everyone** let go at once...
(Pause)
Except for me

A.J. SHAKES HEAD SOLEMNLY

I didn't!

A.J. CASTS THE BALLOON A TENDER PROTECTIVE LOOK

A.J.:   (Slowly)
I just couldn't let go...
(Pause)
And no one noticed.
'Cause every single face was tipping-up
on top of a stretchy neck.

A.J. TILTS HEAD UPWARDS SMOOTHLY FOLLOWING MOVEMENT

(With wonderment)
How quickly those balloons chased upwards
without a sound.
(Sighing)
How little, as they raced across the sky.
(Quietly)
Higher and higher and smaller and smaller,
until they disappeared inside a grey cloud.
All gone!

*A.J. GLIDES ACROSS THE STAGE, MOVES FORWARD
POINTING AT THE BACK OF THE AUDITORIUM*

When I looked down again I knew that every
balloon was not flying away free:
I noticed balloons caught-up in the oldest tree
that grows at the far edge of the big field.
(Sadly)
Balloons of every colour,
crowded-up together on the tangly branches.
(Pause)
Far too many for me to count.

*A.J. GENTLY PULLS THE RED BALLOON NEARER
AND TOUCHES THE SKIN.
A.J.'S FACE LIGHTS UP*

(Quietly)
The old tree looked so beautiful:
just like a Christmas tree...

*A.J. TURNS FROM THE AUDIENCE AND SLOWLY RAISES AN ARM
TO RELEASE THE RED BALLOON.
A.J. WATCHES THE BALLOON FLOAT UPWARDS BEFORE TURNING
TO FACE THE AUDIENCE*

Yesterday was special...

A.J. LOOKS UPWARDS OVER A SHOULDER HIGH IN THE SKY.

CLOCKWORK PERSON

LEE IS A LARGER THAN LIFE CHARACTER WHO CONSTANTLY CHALLENGES AUTHORITY AND FULLY EXPECTS TO BE ON THE WRONG SIDE OF SCHOOL TEACHERS. LEE'S FORTHRIGHT PROVOCATIVE MANNER MASKS INSECURITY BUT IS WRONGLY INTERPRETED AS IMPERTINENCE. BY MIMICKING THE SPEECH AND BODY LANGUAGE OF AGGRESSORS LEE CUTS THEM DOWN TO SIZE AND OUTWARDLY SAILS THROUGH LIFE UNPERTURBED AS ADULTS DESPAIR!

ENTER: LEE, *RUNNING, AN OPEN BAG CONTAINING SCHOOL BOOKS SWINGING CARELESSLY FROM ONE HAND WHILST LEE DEPERATELY WAVES THE FREE HAND HIGH IN THE AIR.*

LEE: **Stop!**

LEE FREEZES, DROPPING THE BAG
SIGHS LOUDLY CASTING EYES SKYWARDS
AND CONSULTS A WRIST-WATCH, MUTTERING UNDER BREATH

(Vehemently)
Missed the bus because of her.

LEE KICKS OUT AT THE BAG

Managed to keep out of her way **all day.**
Then, the moment I thought I'd got away with it.
Just as I'm sliding out of the door, she **pounces.**
(Tossing head in defiance)
Grabs hold of me: and starts going on.
What luck!

LEE WINDS A GIANT IMAGINARY KEY

On, and on and on... about nothing!

LEE SHRUGS

Winding me up!
On and on... before she actually comes out
with something really interesting...
Suddenly, out of the blue she says,
'Haven't you got the brains you were born with?'
(Pause)
Well!
This sets me thinking.
But she cut in, with
'Stop sulking, pleeeeese.'
(Pause)

LEE:
Wasn't exactly sulking, it was more-like wondering.
What happened to the brains?
Where did they go?
Shan't ever know the answer to that one.

LEE WANDERS FORWARD SHAKING HEAD

Didn't listen after that: didn't matter.
She'd been wound-up like a clockwork toy.
And she's got another think coming if she thinks
she's going to wind **me** up! I thought to myself.
(Pause)
Joss has got a frog with a key sticking out
of its side, its got a **really** ugly face.
It hops when you put it down. then slows up
and rocks backwards and forwards without
getting anywhere...
...Then the clicking gets slower and slower.
And it lies there, dead looking.

LEE APES THE ANIMATED TEACHER

No sign of winding-down here, I thought.
She's got a long way to go yet!
Talk about all mouth!
(Pause)
Trouble with being bored is, you can't think of
anything to do.

LEE STANDS ON ONE FOOT

There's counting numbers in your head
standing on one leg, as the mouth goes up and down...

LEE CHANGES LEGS

...And counting down from a hundred.
(Mouthing)
Thirty-One, thirty, twenty-nine...
'Well?...
What do you have to say for yourself?'

LEE CAREFULLY PLACES THE FOOT DOWN AND FREEZES

Oh **no!**
A question.
She's waiting for an answer.

LEE BOWS HEAD AND STARES DOWN AT THE FLOOR

27

LEE: 'Yes, Miss,' or
'No, Miss?'
Haven't a clue.
(Pause)
Her eyes are on my head, she's trying to work out
what happened to the brains I was born with!
She's gone very quiet, I thought... and waited.

LEE LOOKS UP WITH EXTREME CAUTION

When I did look up, she'd **gone.**
What do you make of that?

LEE CHECKS WATCH AND RETRIEVES BAG AND SAUNTERS OFF

EXIT LEE.

PERCY LAMBERT

IN 1907 AN AREA OF MARSHY MEADOWLAND WAS TRANSFORMED INTO A GIANT OVAL CONCRETE TRACK WITH SPECTACULAR BANKED BENDS. THE BROOKLANDS MOTOR COURSE IMMEDIATELY ATTRACTED WORLD-CLASS DRIVERS BATTLING TO ESTABLISH A WORLD LAND-SPEED RECORD. PERCY LAMBERT WAS THE FIRST TO COVER 100 MILES IN AN HOUR – BUT A FRENCHMAN SNATCHED THE RECORD FROM THE BRITISH PUBLIC HERO IN 1913.

A HIGH STOOL CENTRE STAGE, SPADGER IS PERCHED, LEGS DANGLING, CLOSELY EXAMINING AN UNFRAMED SEPIA PHOTOGRAPH. SPADGER'S FATHER IS A LODGEKEEPER AT BROOKLANDS, THE CHILD IDOLISES LAMBERT AND HAS BEEN PRESENT AT THE DRIVERS FREQUENT TRACK VISITS.
SPADGER HAS DEEP POCKETS AND HAS A HABIT OF JAMMING HANDS DOWN DEEP AND WEARS OVERSIZED LACED BOOTS THAT EMPHASISE BARE KNEES.

SPADGER: Thirty-first was a Friday,
that day October last.
(Looking up from the photograph)
And I was there, before the heavy mist
had had a chance to rise.
And Mister Lambert had been patiently waiting
for longer than that.
(Pause)
'Motor racing is that fellow's life',
Father always said.
(Referring to the photograph)
I remember stamping up and down
and blowing into my hands to keep warm.
(Pause)
At last...

SPADGER CLAMBERS DOWN FROM THE STOOL

...The sun broke through.
And I took up position...
(Spadger points to the spot)
...To the side of the start-line.

SPADGER MOVES TO THE SIDE

Mister Lambert was in goggles and helmet:
hunched behind the steering wheel of the Talbot.
(Pause)
I had seen him often enough at the course;
but **never before** that look of determination.
Gosh! My heart began thumping.
(Smiling)

SPADGER: I was caught up in **his** resolve
to regain that World Record.
(Quietly and matter of fact)
Earlier in the week, during practice laps,
Mister Lambert had had one of his 'lucky escapes'
when a tyre burst.
Brand-new cords had since been fitted
with a good dozen bolts fixed to each.
There'd be **no** chance of any of those
moving from the rims.
Everything had been thought of.

SPADGER ANIMATED CRANING TO SEE, DESPERATELY EXCITED

Mister Lambert was revving her hard.
The thunder of the cylinders
grew to a deafening roar...

*SPADGER CLASPS HANDS OVER EARS, THE PHOTOGRAPH
FLUTTERS DOWN UNNOTICED*

...The Talbot scorched from the line.
(Pause)
I ran over to Member's Bridge
fast as my legs could carry me.
Best place to watch from.
(Shrugging)
No one else was there though.
Not that day.
(Pause)
From the bridge I could hear the approach of the car...

SPADGER POINTS TOWARDS THE DISTANT HILL

...Behind the hill, before it shot out
gaining speed, high on the banking, closer and closer:
until it flashed by right under my feet.
And the bridge trembled; and it was gone.

SPADGER LEANS FORWARD WAVING WILDLY

I leaned over the parapet every time he lapped.
Waved, shouted, 'Good Luck!'
Even though I knew he could not see or hear.
(Pause)
The Talbot hurtled round.
(Growing more and more excited)
Again and again.
Golly! The **speed!**
He must have covered twenty laps.
The Record was in the bag.

SPADGER: (Pause)
Next time around
I was listening out for the car: I heard it
roaring towards me, hidden from sight by the hill.
BANG!
(A long pause)

SPADGER IS BEWILDERED

(Gasp)
A tyre?
The car catapulted into view swerving wildly.

SPADGER: POINTING DESPERATELY

A tyre **had** burst.
(Pause)
And Mister Lambert was fighting for control:
my heart was in my mouth.
Suddenly, the car shot right up onto the very top
of the banking: and off!
Skidding along, spraying up sand from the other side.
(Pause)
My hero! Struggled for his life.
(Quietly)
I dared not look; yet dared not take my eyes away.

SPADGER STARES INTO THE MIDDLE DISTANCE IN A TRANCE

The car travelled a little distance
before it tipped
and began to roll.
Over and over and over.
(Gasp)
Mister Lambert was flung high into the air:
landed face-down on the track...

SPADGER WIPES A HAND ACROSS MOUTH, BITES LOWER LIP

...He lay, without moving.
But he breathed; I was close enough to see.
(Pause)
The car rolled on.
(With terror)
Splintering wood, tearing metal!
As it careered into the bridge:
smashed to smithereens.
(Pause)
The car stood upright against the bridge.

SPADGER LOOKS BACK TOWARDS THE HILL

31

SPADGER: Looking back, torn shreds of tyre, wild patterns
burnt into the track...
...And quietness.
I leaned against the parapet...
(Pause)
...numbed.
(A long pause)
Men appeared: rushed to his side.
The limp form was loaded into the Brookland's ambulance.

SPADGER WIPES NOSE ON A SLEEVE, SNIFFS.

And that was to be the last I saw of Mister Lambert, alive.

*SPADGER NOTICES THE PHOTOGRAPH, PICKING IT UP
LOOKS AFFECTIONATELY AT THE IMAGE*

He passed away before reaching
the Cottage Hospital.
(Pause)
I would never see him again.
(Whispering)
But I was mistaken.

SPADGER LOOKS AROUND

Just now; almost a year later.
On a deserted course; standing on Member's Bridge, alone.
(Listening hard)
I **heard** the sound of Mister Lambert's Talbot
roaring invisibly around the banking.
(Pause)
Then... I actually **saw** the car,
with him at the wheel!
Must have travelled for a hundred feet or more...
(Incredulously)
Before it vanished into thin air.

SPADGER CLASPS HANDS OVER EARS WHILST SHYING AWAY

(Shouting)
Splintering wood, tearing metal.
(Pause)
When I dared to look below the bridge...
...Nothing!

SPADGER CLAMBERS ONTO THE STOOL

Mister Lambert is out there, chasing that record.
(Smiling down at the photograph)
Motor racing was that fellow's life.

THE PRESENT

ZIGGY IS A LIVELY UNCOMPLICATED CHILD CELEBRATING A BIRTHDAY. ZIGGY IS YOUNG ENOUGH TO THINK OF THE DAY AS WONDERFULLY SPECIAL – BECAUSE OF THE PRESENTS!

A HUGE BRIGHTLY GIFT-WRAPPED SQUARE PRESENT WITH AN ENORMOUS BOW DOMINATES A LOW TABLE STANDING IN A PROMINENT POSITION.

ENTER: ZIGGY, *RUSHING FROM NOWHERE WITH THE INTENTION OF PASSING THROUGH. ZIGGY CATCHES SIGHT OF THE ENTICING PRESENT ALMOST TOO LATE AND IS FORCED TO TURN BACK BEFORE HURRYING TOWARDS IT. ZIGGY STOPS DEAD, AS IF INSTANTLY TURNED TO STONE AND STARES AT THE PRESENT WITH OPEN-MOUTHED SILENT FASCINATION.*

ZIGGY: Ohhh!

ZIGGY SLOWLY EXTENDS A HAND AS IF TO TOUCH BUT HESITATES AND WITHDRAWS AS IF IT WOULD BE TERRIBLY WRONG TO DO SO

Oh! What?
(Pause)
Is that fantastic?
Or fantastic?
Or what!

ZIGGY STANDS BACK AND SAVOURS THE MAGIC OF SURPRISE BEFORE ALLOWING A NOISY INTAKE OF BREATH TO ESCAPE

What can it be?

ZIGGY CIRCLES THE TABLE WITHOUT ONCE TAKING EYES OFF THE PRESENT

Who's it from?
Can't see a card to say who it's from.

ZIGGY VIEWS THE PRESENT FROM EVERY POSSIBLE ANGLE

No clues!

ZIGGY STARES LONG AND HARD

(Anxiously)
Perhaps it's not for me!
(Pause)
Got to be; it's **my** birthday.
(Happily)
It's my birthday; so it must be for me!

ZIGGY MAKES A MOVE TO PICK UP THE PRESENT BUT FALTERS AT THE LAST MOMENT

But I've **had** all my presents.
Could be a trick.

ZIGGY: A **mean** trick.
(Pause)
Suppose it's just an empty cardboard box...
...with nothing inside.
A thrown-away box wrapped up fancy
so I **think** I'm getting something really special...

ZIGGY LOOKS AROUND SUSPICIOUSLY

Then, when I open it up
they'll all jump out and crowd around.
(Pause)
And they'll all laugh at me; and I'll have
to pretend that I thought the joke funny too!

*ZIGGY LOOKS FROM THE PRESENT TO THE FAR CORNERS
AND BACK AGAIN*

I'd **hate** that to happen.

ZIGGY CHEWS ON A FINGERNAIL NERVOUSLY

Surely not!
No one'd do that to me.
Would they?

*ZIGGY CAUTIOUSLY APPROACHES THE PRESENT AND LEANS OVER
AND SNIFFS BUT THE PRESENT REMAINS AS MYSTERIOUS AS EVER*

Suppose I just walk away,
ignore it.
That would spoil their fun.
That's the answer.

*ZIGGY TURNS AND MOVES AWAY FROM THE TABLE
THEN SPINS AND QUICKLY SNATCHES UP THE PRESENT AND
SHAKES IT HARD BEFORE REPLACING IT CAREFULLY AND
PRECISELY*

It rattles!
There's something in there.
But... **what?**
(A long pause)
I've **got** to know!

*ZIGGY SNATCHES OFF THE RIBBON AND TEARS PAPER IN A
FRENZIED ATTACK ON THE PRESENT BEFORE PEERING INSIDE
ZIGGY'S FACE IS A PICTURE OF HAPPINESS*

Ohhh! WHAT?
Is that **fantastic!**

ZIGGY GRABS THE BOX AND RACES OFF

EXIT ZIGGY.

GREEN FLOYD

JAY IS MAKING TRACKS FOR HOME ACCOMPANIED BY A FRIEND (THE UNSEEN FRIEND IS OFF STAGE IN THE WINGS). THE SCHOOL DAY HAS TAKEN ITS INEVITABLE TOLL ON JAY'S PERSONAL APPEARANCE AND UNTIDY HAIR TOGETHER WITH A LONG SOCK WRINKLING AROUND AN ANKLE AND SCHOOL TIE FLAGGING AT HALF-MAST PROCLAIM A PERSONALITY WITH A LIVELY ENTHUSIASM FOR PLAY AND CASUAL ATTITUDE TOWARDS FORMAL STUDY.

ENTER: JAY, *TO THE REAR OF THE STAGE WALKING SIDE BY SIDE WITH THE FRIEND FOLLOWING THE LINE OF THE WINGS TOWARDS THE FRONT. THE TWO FRIENDS HAVE BEGUN AN ARGUMENT AND JAY'S FACE TURNS TOWARDS THE FRIEND. JAY STOPS ABRUPTLY.*

JAY: (Shouting)
Floyd's **not!**

JAY SWINGS TO CONFRONT THE FRIEND

(Shouting)
He's **NOT!**

JAY TAKES SEVERAL STEPS BACKWARDS TO DISTANCE FROM THE FRIEND BEFORE STANDING GROUND, AGGRESSIVELY AND SHAKING A FIST IN THREATENING MANNER

Huh!
You want'er see something **really** ugly?
(Pause)
Try looking in the mirror, then!

*JAY TURNS TO FACE THE FRONT
JAY'S FACE SLOWLY REGISTERS DISGUST IN RESPONSE TO UNHEARD INSULTS
JAY'S HEAD TURNS SHARPLY TO ADDRESS THE FRIEND*

Floyd, **thick?**

JAY SLOWLY TURNS FACE AND LOOKS STRAIGHT AHEAD

THICK!

JAY SHRUGS A SHOULDER

No.
(Shaking head)
He's not exactly... thick:
he's bright enough in his own way.

PAUSE FOR AN UNHEARD COMMENT

JAY: Floyd's just not the same as us,
he's... different, that's all.

JAY MOVES FORWARD A PACE OR TWO
JAY STOPS ABRUPTLY AND TURNS HEAD SHARPLY IN RESPONSE
TO AN UNHEARD TAUNT

Say that again!
If you dare.

JAY WALKS FORWARD HAUGHTILY (TO THE EDGE OF THE STAGE)
AND TURNS SHARPLY AT A NINETY DEGREE ANGLE
JAY FREEZES AND TURNS FACE TOWARDS THE FRIEND (NEWLY
POSITIONED IN THE AUDITORIUM)

Common yourself!

JAY SWINGS BODY ROUND TO SQUARELY FACE THE FRIEND

Nothing wrong with his being common;
suits him being common.
It's quite in order for **him** to be common...

JAY POINTS AN ACCUSATORY FINGER

...You're the one that's out of order!
And...
(Sneering)
...Common!

JAY PAUSES FOR A BRIEF UNHEARD RETORT

You're only jealous.

JAY TURNS AND BEGINS TO FOLLOW THE LINE OF THE STAGE
HEADING IN THE DIRECTION OF THE OPPOSITE WINGS
JAY STOPS ABRUPTLY AND TURNS SLOWLY TO FACE THE
FRIEND WHO IS KEEPING PACE

But he can't speak up for himself.
Can't talk, can he?
(Quietly)
Pity you're not more like him!
(Fondly)
He's special.

JAY TURNS AND PRESENTS BACK OF BODY POINTEDLY
BEFORE SPINNING BACK TO FACE THE FRIEND ANGRILY

That's just where you're wrong.
(Defensively)
Floyd isn't a slimy stinker!

JAY: He's always in the bath; he's always bathing.
He's more particular than you:
Floyd's **very** particular.

*JAY AND FRIEND WALK ALONG SIDE BY SIDE WITH JAY LISTENING
TO AN UNHEARD REQUEST.
JAY STOPS AND STARES OPEN-MOUTHED*

Come round to see Floyd!
After all the things you've been saying about him
behind his back.
You've gotta be joking.
(Pause)
Anyway! What makes you think he'll wanta see you?
He won't will he?
Not after I've finished telling him what you've
been saying about him.

JAY SMILES SARCASTICALLY AND SHAKES HEAD NEGATIVELY

Too late!
Too late for any of that old flannel.
No use being nice, now!

*JAY TURNS AND TAKES A FEW STEPS
AND CALLS OVER A SHOULDER*

Anyway Floyd's probably having a little lie down
usually does around this time of day...

JAY TURNS ATTENTION TO THE GROUND AHEAD

(Quietly)
...gets tired out by the afternoons.

*JAY STOPS AND STIFFENS AND STANDS VERY STILL
BEFORE REACTING TO THE UNHEARD INSULT BY TURNING
SLOWLY AND DELIBERATELY (A NINETY DEGREE ANGLE)*

(Pained and hurt)
And a fine friend **you've** turned out to be, too!
(Pause)
All right! Come round if you must.
(Hastily)
Just this once, mind!
So long as you're quiet and don't upset him.
(Pause)
You can give him his tea...
...if that's what you want.

JAY: But remember,
Floyd's not like us.
(Smiling)
He's special, even though you could say he's just
a common iguana.
(Pause)
To him you're just a common human, even though
you're special to your Mum and Dad.
Got that?

JAY SMILES AND POINTS THE WAY

Come on!
Let's go see Green Floyd!

JAY RUSHES OFF WITH THE FRIEND

EXIT JAY.

THE LITTLE MATCH GIRL

A BITTERLY COLD NEW YEAR'S EVE AND SNOW IS FALLING AS THE MATCH GIRL WANDERS THE DARK DESERTED STREETS OF THE CITY. SHE IS HUNGRY AND MISERABLE YET TOO AFRAID TO RETURN HOME BECAUSE SHE HAS NOT MANAGED TO SELL ANY MATCHES AND HAS CAUSE TO FEAR ANOTHER BEATING FROM HER BRUTAL FATHER.

THE TIRED LOOKING MATCH GIRL IS BAREFOOTED AND INADEQUATELY DRESSED IN A THIN SHAWL. SHE CARRIES A BOX OF EXTRA LONG HOUSEHOLD MATCHES AND WANDERS FORWARD AIMLESSLY.

MATCH GIRL: (Quietly almost to herself)
Matches...
...matches.

SHE SINKS DOWN AND SITS HUDDLED UP AGAINST THE COLD.SHE CLUTCHES HER KNEES BEFORE CHANGING POSITION AND PLACING THE MATCHBOX IN HER LAP AND EXERCISING STIFF FINGERS

Matches.

*SHE RUBS HER HANDS TOGETHER AND ATTEMPTS TO BLOW WARMTH INTO HER FINGERTIPS BEFORE HER ATTENTION IS CAUGHT BY THE MATCHBOX
SHE PICKS UP THE BOX THOUGHTFULLY
SHE OPENS THE MATCHBOX AND TAKES OUT A MATCH*

Just one.
(Pause)
Surely one match won't be missed?

SHE LOOKS AROUND GUILTILY

Who's to know?
Just this one to warm my hands.

SHE STRIKES THE MATCH AND HOLDS IT AT ARMS LENGTH

(Smiling)
Oh! A little candle.
And such warmth from a little thing.

SHE STARES INTO THE FLAME

There is a picture in the flame...
(Gasp)
...Why! A stove!
(Excited)
Look!

MATCH GIRL: A black stove with gleaming polished feet and handles.
And bright flames dancing out of the open door.
(Pause)
I have never seen a fire such as this;
never seen wood that could spark and blaze so warmly.

SHE LEANS CLOSE TO THE FLAME AND SMILES
SHE WIGGLES HER TOES CONTENTEDLY
BEFORE SHAKING THE MATCH TO EXTINGUISH THE FLAME
SHE STARES AT THE BURNT-OUT MATCH SADLY
AND LOOKS AROUND SEARCHINGLY BEFORE THROWING
DOWN THE SPENT MATCH

(Whispering)
Gone!

SHE HUDDLES AND HUGS HER KNEES TIGHTLY

The wonderful warm stove, gone.

SHE SNATCHES UP THE MATCHBOX AND HASTILY STRIKES
A SECOND MATCH

Where's the stove?

SHE PEERS INTO THE FLAME

It must be there, somewhere!
(Pause)
Oh!
(Smiling)
No stove...
...instead, I am looking into a furnished room.
I see a table spread with a heavy snow white cloth...
...And fine china plates with pretty blue patterns.
And folded napkins at two place settings.
(Pause)
Food!
Oh! This table is overloaded with food.

HER MOUTH FALLS OPEN
SHE GASPS

A **huge** roast goose with crisp golden skin.
Yes! Stuffed full of apples and prunes...
...Steaming hot; sitting in the very centre of
the table.

HER EYES GROW WIDE AND SHE SAVOURS THE SMELL

MATCH GIRL: A silver carving knife rests against the goose...

SHE LICKS HER LIPS AND STRETCHES OUT A HAND

...It is time to carve.

SHE SHAKES THE MATCHSTICK AND THE FLAME DIES
SHE STARES AROUND DESPERATELY

Oh, no!
Nothing to be seen now.
Nothing but an empty alleyway.

SHE STRIKES ANOTHER MATCH

What next I wonder?

SHE KNEELS AND LOOKS UPWARDS TO A GREAT HEIGHT

(With wonderment)
A beautiful, **beautiful** Christmas tree.
Even more beautifully decked than the one
I peeped at through the windows of the great house
belonging to a rich merchant.
(Gleefully)
And this is far bigger.
Look! Thousand upon thousand lighted candles.
Why! This must be the most splendid sight
I shall ever see...

SHE STRETCHES OUT HER HANDS AND HASTILY SHAKES THE
MATCHSTICK AND THROWS THE SPENT MATCH ASIDE WHILST
CONTINUING TO LOOK UPWARDS
SHE LOOKS HIGHER STILL UNTIL SHE LOOKS DIRECTLY
OVERHEAD

Wait!... The candles, the candles are floating up.
Up and up, higher and higher.

SHE RISES TO HER FEET

(With bitter disappointment)
Those are not candles at all;
those are stars.
I have been looking at the stars, no more than that.

SHE WANDERS FORWARD IDLY ABSORBED IN THE NIGHT SKY
HER HAND SHOOTS SKYWARDS BEFORE ARCING
HER FACE IS GRAVE

A shooting star...
(Long pause)

MATCH GIRL: ...A child is dying.
Dear Grandmother used to say,
'When a star falls from the sky a gentle child's
soul is taken straight up to heaven.'

SHE HASTILY RETRIEVES THE MATCHBOX AND STRIKES THE
THREE REMAINING MATCHES AT ONCE BEFORE THROWING
DOWN THE EMPTY MATCHBOX
SHE LOOKS INTO THE BRIGHT FLAME

(Happily)
Grandmother, dear!
I see you clearly in the circle of flame.
Why! The light is brighter than day,
brighter than sunshine.
(With amazement)
You look so lovely, so gentle and happy.
Even kinder and more gentle than I remember.
(Pause)
Please, please...
...Take me with you.
(Wistfully)
Otherwise you will vanish when the match goes out.
(Pause)
Like the warm stove...
...the delicious goose
...and the beautiful Christmas tree.

SHE LOOKS LONGINGLY INTO THE FLAME
SHE SMILES AND BLOWS OUT THE MATCHES
BEFORE RAISING HER ARMS TO BE TAKEN

Take me with you.

THE MATCH GIRL SINKS DOWN AND CLOSES HER EYES

THE BAIT MACHINE

A FISHING BAIT VENDING MACHINE IS SIMILAR TO A DRINKS DISPENSING MACHINE IN BOTH DESIGN CONCEPT AND SCALE.

N.B. THE BAIT MACHINE IS POSITIONED CENTRALLY AND JUST BEYOND THE FRONT EDGE OF THE STAGE.

TERRY IS A NATURALLY CURIOUS AND EXPRESSIVE CHARACTER. TERRY'S CASUAL AND RELAXED PERSONALITY IS REFLECTED IN A CASUAL STYLE OF DRESS. TERRY IS WEARING A JACKET/JEANS WITH POCKETS THAT CONTAIN A FEW EMPTY SWEET WRAPPERS AND A HANDFUL OF LOOSE CHANGE. TERRY IS VERY LIKEABLE AND UNCOMPLICATED.

TERRY *WANDERS INTO VIEW AND CROSSES THE STAGE AT A RELAXED PACE. TERRY CATCHES SIGHT OF THE STRANGE NOVEL DEVICE AND STOPS DEAD. THE CHILD EYES THE BAIT MACHINE WITH ASTONISHMENT AND A LITTLE SUSPICION.*

TERRY: That wasn't there yesterday!

TERRY CARRIES OUT A VISUAL EXAMINATION OF THE FRONT AND SIDES OF THE MACHINE

Well!

TERRY USES BOTH HANDS TO DRAW THE OUTLINE SHAPE OF THE TOWERING RECTANGULAR FORM BEFORE STEPPING BACKWARDS AND VIEWING THE MACHINE WITH GREAT SUSPICION

A **fishing bait** machine!

TERRY STEPS CLOSER AND USES A FINGER TO TRACE A LINE OF LETTERING

(Reading with exaggeration)
Fisshing baait.

TERRY LOOKS AROUND AND SHAKES HEAD

Don't see too many fishermen round here.
Come to that, don't see any fishermen at all!
(Smiling)
Like the pictures of the fish on the machine.
They're same as the ones outside the fish
and chip shop down the road...
...lively and cheerful looking...
(Tilting head quizzically)
...standing up on their tails,
ready to leap for joy.

TERRY: These here've got more reason to be cheerful, too!
With a machine stacked full of bait right behind.
No wonder they're blowing bubbles!

*TERRY JUMPS OFF THE GROUND IN AN ATTEMPT TO SEE THE TOP
OF THE VENDING MACHINE BEFORE BENDING DOWN AND
CRAWLING ON HANDS AND KNEES IN AN EFFORT TO LOOK
UNDERNEATH BEFORE STANDING ON ONE LEG AND CRANING
ROUND TO SEE BEHIND
TERRY CONSIDERS BEFORE MOVING CLOSE AND SNIFFING*

Don't smell!

TERRY RE-READS THE LINE OF LETTERING

Fisshing baait
Bag-it with Mag-it!
(Pause)
And **there's** the pictures of the Mag-its...
...corny and flesh pink with little stumpy arms.
And they're all smiling up at the fish!
Well!

*TERRY MOVES CLOSER AND BENDS TO READ FIVE BOXES SET AT
WAIST HEIGHT ON THE FRONT PANEL OF THE MACHINE BUT SET
TO ONE SIDE*

Bronze maggots, one pound fifty.
White maggots, one pound fifty.
Red maggots...
(Pulling a face)
...one pound fifty.
Mixed maggots, same price
and **Casters!**
(Shrugging)
ditto, ditto.
(Pause)
They all cost exactly the same!

*TERRY LEANS CLOSE AND POINTS OUT AN INSTRUCTION
POSITIONED BENEATH THE FIVE BOXES*

Hang on!
What's this?
(Reading with exaggeration)
When red light shows **ON...**
...Select another.

TERRY SCRATCHES HEAD

TERRY: Come on, now!
(Pause)
So if it's out of bronze Mag-its try another colour?
So, does it matter what colour in the first place?
What's the difference
as far as the fish dangling on a hook is concerned?
(Pause)
If it doesn't matter, then you might just as well
close your eyes and take a stab in the dark.
(Pause)
Why not!

TERRY TAKES A CRITICAL LOOK AT THE MACHINE

And there's another notice!
(Reading with exaggeration)
Mag-it recommends that the maggots in these tubs
are emptied into a normal bait box...
...Mmmmmm...

TERRY STEPS BACK A PACE

...Mmmmm...
Tubs! Of Mag-its!

TERRY SMILES IMPISHLY

Like tubs of ice-cream!
(Pause)
There's **more.**
(Reading with exaggeration)
Allow maggots to recover for sixty minutes
at normal room temperature.
(Pause)
The maggots must feel much the same as I did
after I'd had my tonsils out, I suppose.
Must've taken me about an hour to recover
from the anaesthetic, at room temperature!
Mmmm.

TERRY CLOSES ON THE MACHINE

Look!
(Reading with exaggeration)
Lift flap for product.

TERRY FLIPS THE FLAP

There's a **massive** hole in there!
(Pause)

TERRY: The Mag-its must shoot out've the machine.
And land in the tray feeling woozy,
like they've had their tonsils out!

TERRY PLACES AN EAR AGAINST THE MACHINE

Got it!
Thought so, it's like a fridge in there.

*TERRY HASTILY EMPTIES OUT THE CONTENTS OF A POCKET AND
STUFFS BACK THE EMPTY SWEET WRAPPERS BEFORE COUNTING
THE SMALL CHANGE
TERRY GLANCES UP AT THE MACHINE*

(Reading with exaggeration)
Tens, twenties, fifties and pound coins only.
No change given.

*TERRY COUNTS OUT SMALL CHANGE, ADDING UP UNDER THE
BREATH.
TERRY LOOKS AT THE MACHINE BEFORE TIPPING THE COINAGE
BACK INTO THE POCKET.*

Haven't got enough!
So it's ice-cream.

TERRY RUNS OFF

EXIT TERRY.

Further copies of The Sieve
may be obtained from selected
bookshops or direct from:

Dramatic Lines
PO Box 201
Twickenham
TW2 5RQ
England

@ £4.99 each plus 80p postage & packing
   ($9.99 each plus $4.00 postage & packing Canada)

To: Dramatic Lines PO Box 201, Twickenham, TW2 5RQ, England.

Please send me .... copies of The Sieve

@ £4.99 each plus 80p postage & packing
($9.99 each plus $4.00 postage & packing Canada)

Please make cheque/PO payable to Dramatic Lines

Name ....

Address ....

....

.... Postcode..............................

Scenes fom **The Sieve** have won drama competitions during trials. The Publisher would be interested to hear of any success achieved using this material.

Please send details to:

Dramatic Lines
PO Box 201
Twickenham
TW2 5RQ
England

These will be listed in the reprint. This is Dramatic Lines way of recognising talent and achievement in drama and providing encouragement for young people.

Cabbage, the second book of solo scenes will be available soon.